The King is Born

What Christmas is About

Decorate these circles as Christmas ornaments
or happy faces!

Gabriel is an Archangel.

Gabriel the Archangel was sent to tell Mary that God had chosen her to be the mother of His Son.

Saint Joseph was a carpenter. There are 6 hidden objects here. Can you find them?

Elizabeth was very happy to see her cousin, Mary, the mother of our Lord.

This nice Christmas tree is bare. Add
decorations and then color the picture!

The Roman soldier reads a new law. Joseph and Mary will have to travel to Bethlehem.

Joseph and Mary need to find their way to Bethlehem. Can you help them?

All the inns are full! Poor Joseph and Mary have nowhere to stay.

God provided a place for His Son to be born. It wasn't fancy, but it was warm. Connect the dots and see the first bed that little Jesus slept in.

Jesus, Mary, and Joseph: what a wonderful family!

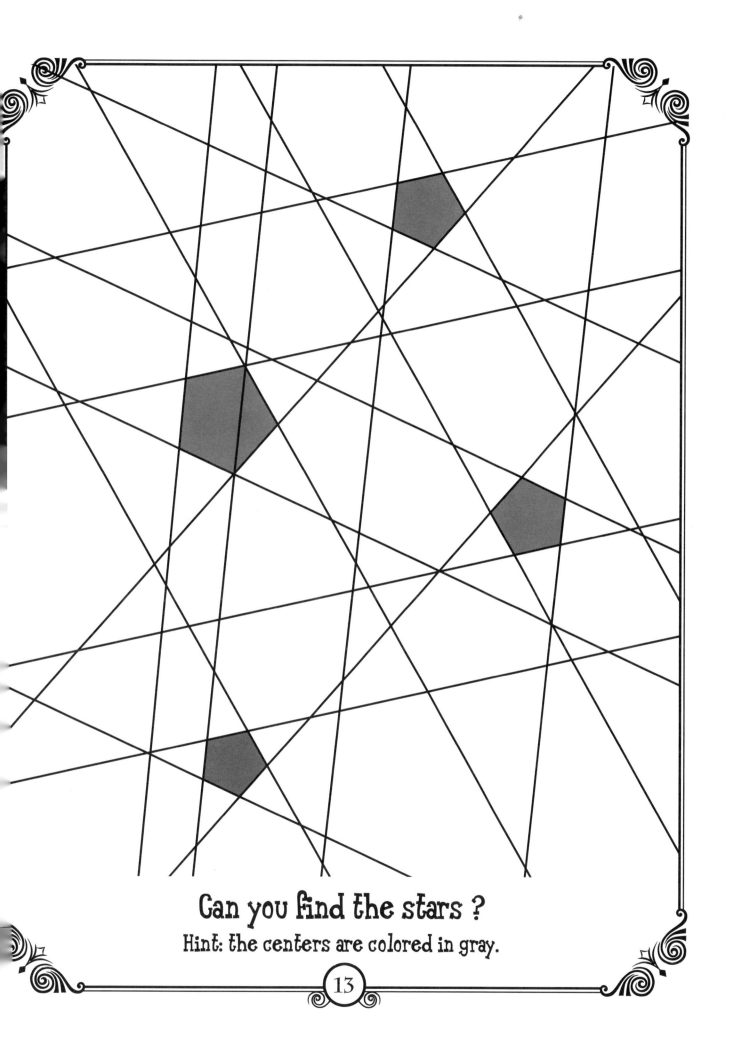

Can you find the stars ?

Hint: the centers are colored in gray.

When Jesus was born, the angels sang praises!

The Holy Family

Dear Jesus, thank You for all my blessings!
Help me to remember that Christmas is really
all about You! Thank You for being my Savior.
Amen.